MOVIE MONSTER MAZES

Vladimir Koziakin

tempo
books

GROSSET & DUNLAP
A FILMWAYS COMPANY
Publishers • New York

BY *Vladimir Koziakin*

Available from
Grosset & Dunlap Publishers

MAZES
MAZES 2
MAZES 3
MAZES 4
MAZES 5
ABC MAZES
ASTRO MAZES
MYSTERY MAZES
DINOSAUR MAZES
MAZES FOR FUN 1
MAZES FOR FUN 2
MAZES FOR FUN 3
MAZES FOR FUN 4
SHARKMAZE
HAUNTED MAZES
AMERICA MAZES

Copyright © 1976 by Vladimir Koziakin
All Rights Reserved
ISBN: 0-448-12628-1
Tempo Books is registered in the U.S. Patent Office
A Tempo Books Original
Published simultaneously in Canada
Printed in the United States of America

MAZES AND MOVIE MONSTERS
A Bone-Chilling Double Feature!

You can almost smell the popcorn, right?
These movie freaks are <u>really</u> freaks, if you
know what I mean. In fact, I had a terrible
time wrangling them down from the silver
screen. But here they are! Half-a-hundred
hungry horrors—dazed, crazed, and waiting
to be mazed!

If you've done mazes before, you can skip
what I'm about to say. If you haven't, follow
the bouncing ball:

Take a sharp pencil and start where the arrow
points in. Now, try to find the one clear path
through the maze—until you come to the spot
where the arrow points out.

"Easy," right? That's what Dr. Jekyll said
when they told him to stop drinking. If you
think you're so smart, just try beating my
murderously mathematically Rated Time
Limits! That'll put you in your place!

And one more thing—I do recommend work-
ing these mazes in asbestos gloves. Some of
the creatures pictured herein are truly too
hot to handle.

Dare to turn the page? As Count Dracula once
said to a weary traveller, "Be my guest!"

Vladimir Koziakin

Maze 1

DR. DEATH
(THE CRIMSON GHOST)

Rated Time Limit/3:30

Maze 2
THEM
Rated Time Limit/4:30

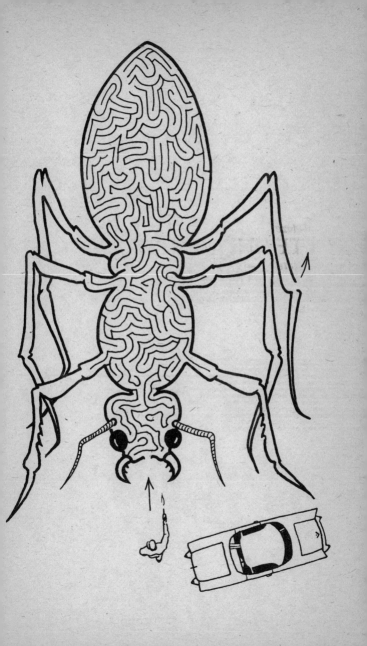

Maze 3

IT CONQUERED
THE WORLD
Rated Time Limit/6:00

Maze 4

CYCLOPS
(THE SEVENTH VOYAGE
OF SINBAD)

Rated Time Limit/4:00

Maze 5

MOTHRA

Rated Time Limit/3:30

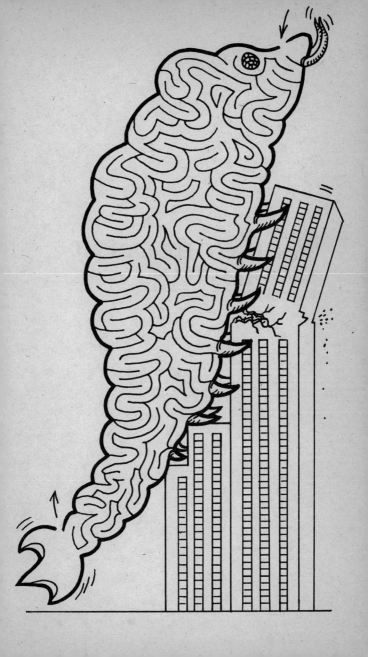

Maze 6

THE DAY THE EARTH
STOOD STILL

Rated Time Limit/4:30

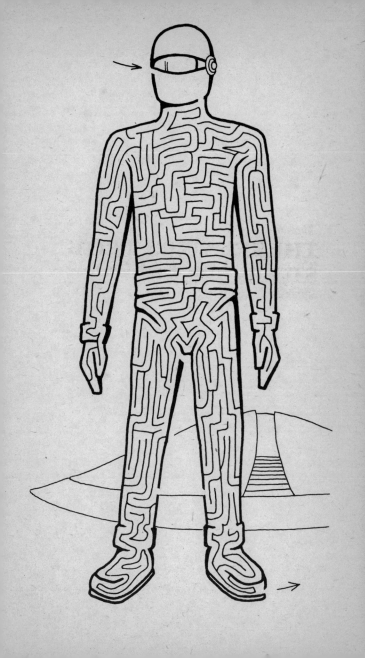

Maze 7

THE CREATURE FROM
THE BLACK LAGOON

Rated Time Limit/6:00

Maze 8

FRANKENSTEIN'S MONSTER

Rated Time Limit/3:00

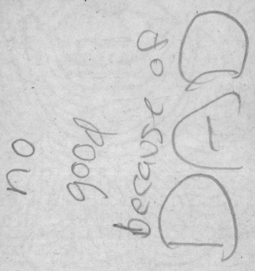

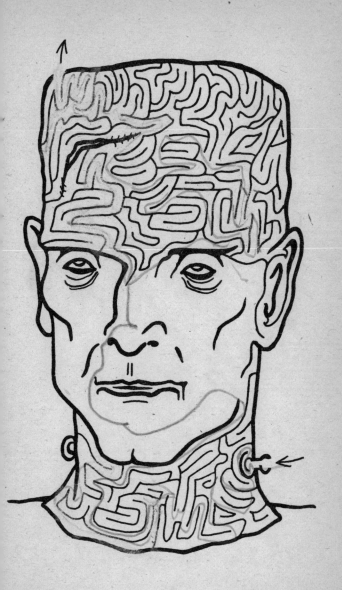

Maze 9

THE BRIDE OF FRANKENSTEIN

Rated Time Limit/2:30

Maze 10

FRANKENSTEIN'S
DAUGHTER

Rated Time Limit/7:00

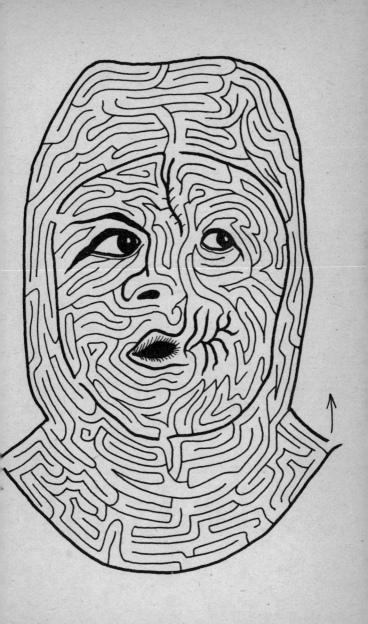

Maze 11

THE FLY

Rated Time Limit/5:30

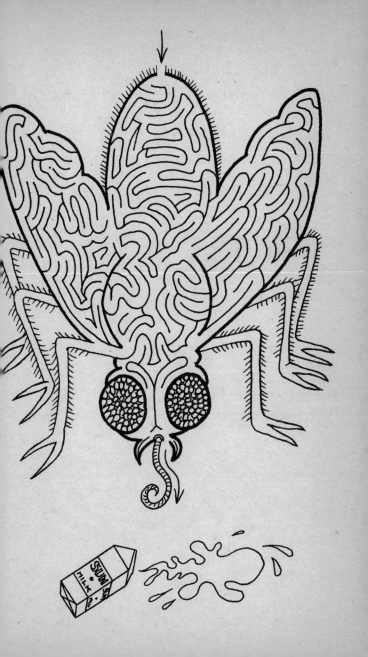

Maze 12

GODZILLA

Rated Time Limit/6:00

Maze 13

ROSEMARY'S BABY

Rated Time Limit/4:30

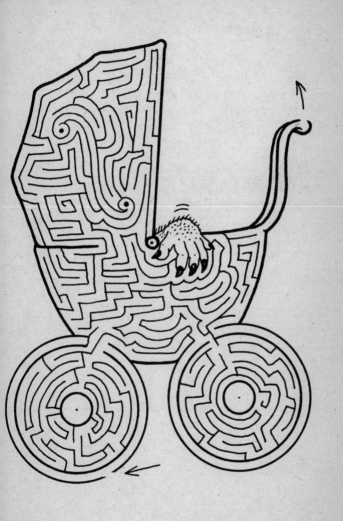

Maze 14

BEN

Rated Time Limit/1:30

It took me 32 seconds.

RODAN

Rated Time Limit/6:30

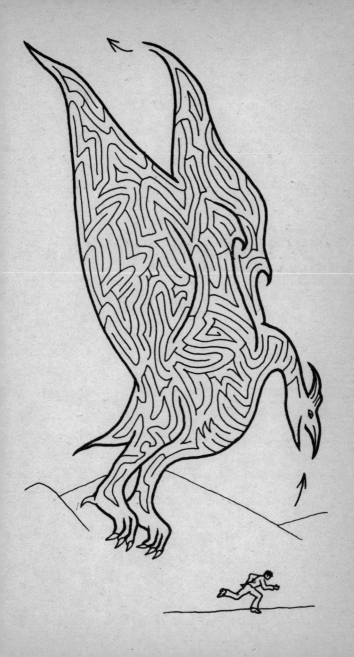

Maze 16

DRACULA'S DAUGHTER

Rated Time Limit/7:30

MIGHTY JOE YOUNG

Rated Time Limit/5:00

Maze 18

INVASION OF
THE SAUCER MEN
Rated Time Limit/7:30

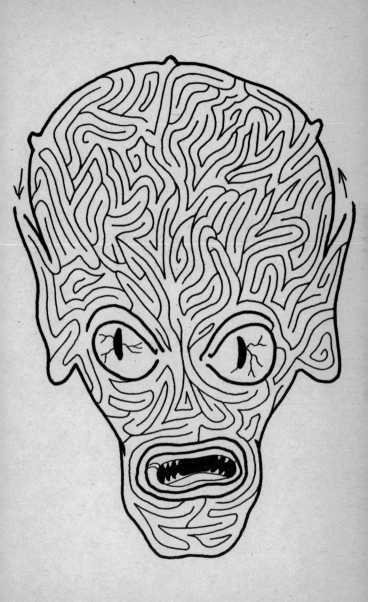

Maze 19

GIDRA

Rated Time Limit/5:30

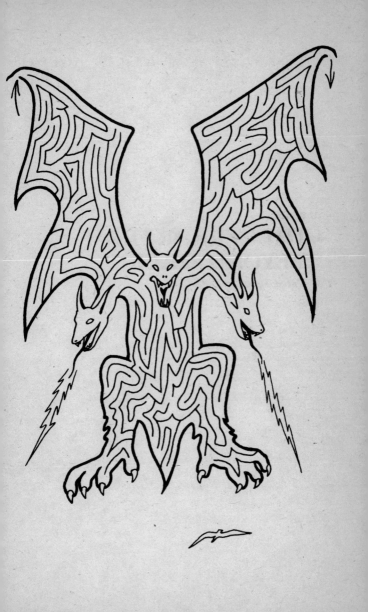

Maze 20

THE TERROR FROM BEYOND SPACE

Rated Time Limit/8:00

Maze 21
GORGO
Rated Time Limit/4:00

WAR OF THE WORLDS (MARTIAN)

Rated Time Limit/6:30

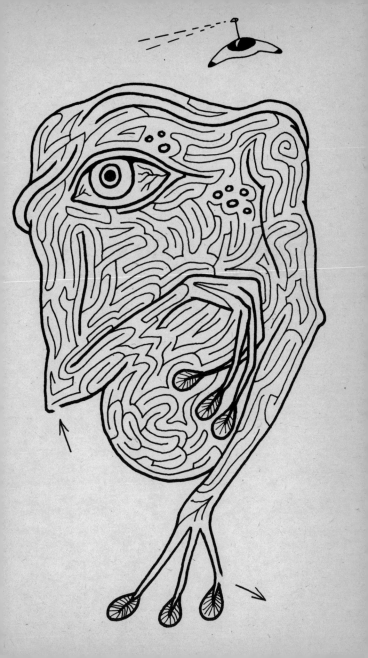

Maze 23

THE SUN DEMON

Rated Time Limit/7:00

FORBIDDEN PLANET (ROBBIE THE ROBOT)

Rated Time Limit/5:00

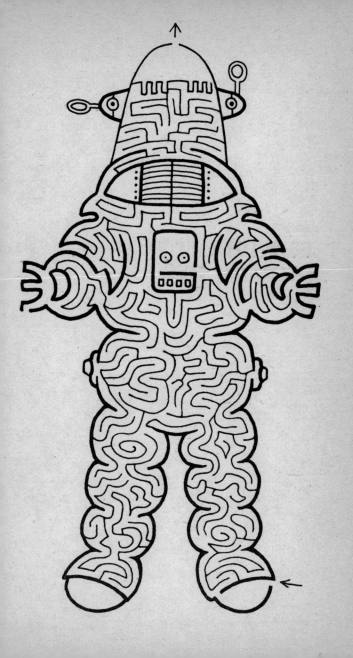

THE PHANTOM OF THE OPERA

Rated Time Limit/6:30

Maze 26

DONOVAN'S BRAIN

Rated Time Limit/4:30

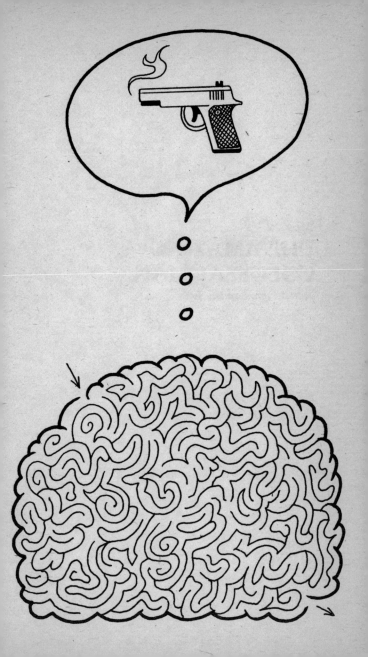

THE AMAZING COLOSSAL MAN

Rated Time Limit/5:30

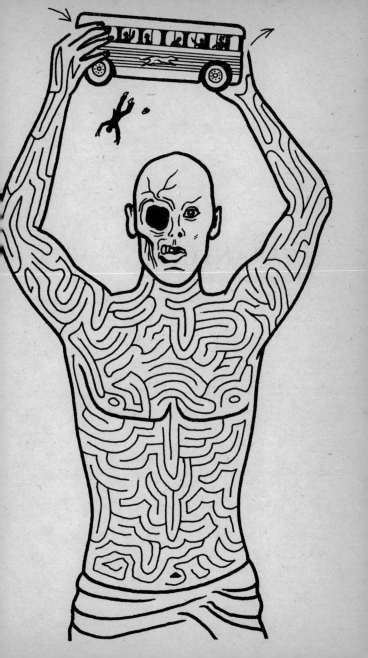

GARANTULA

Rated Time Limit/2:00

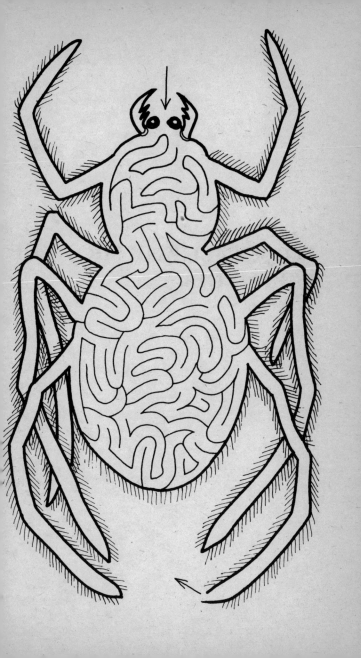

Maze 29

DR. JEKYLL AND MR. HYDE
(MR. HYDE)

Rated Time Limit/8:30

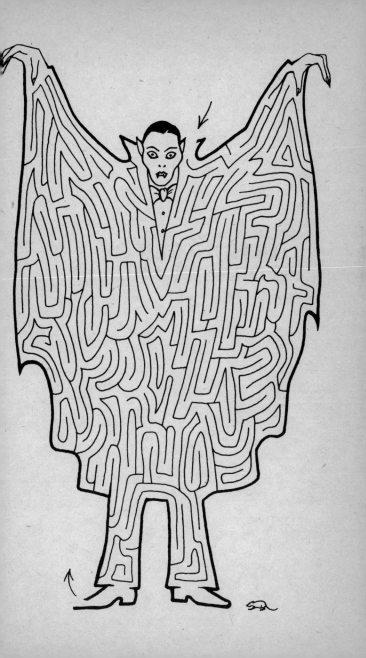

THE MONSTER OF PIEDRAS BLANCAS

Rated Time Limit/6:30

Maze 32

THE BLOB

Rated Time Limit/5:00

Maze 33
SQUIRM
Rated Time Limit/7:00

Maze 34
IGOR
Rated Time Limit/3:30

I did it in

1:30

Maze 35

THE GHOUL

Rated Time Limit/8:00

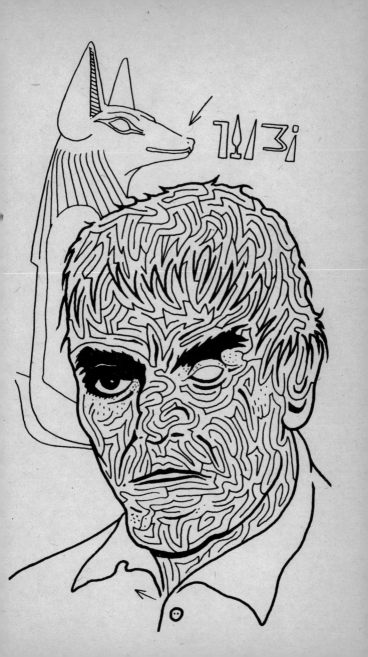

IT CAME FROM
OUTER SPACE

Rated Time Limit/6:30

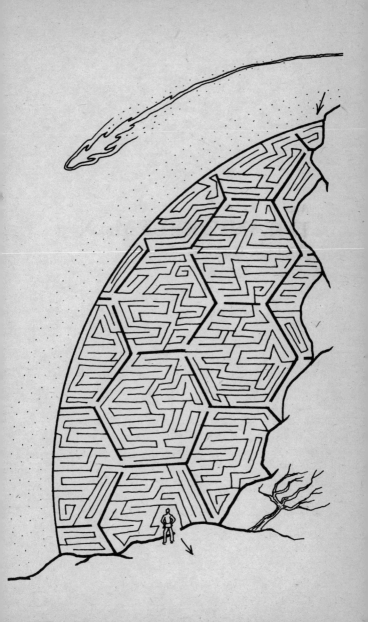

Maze 37

THE INVISIBLE MAN

Rated Time Limit/3:00

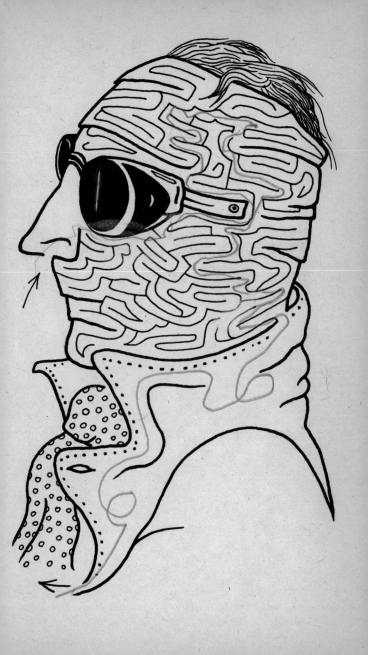

TWENTY MILLIONS MILES TO EARTH (GIANT YMU)

Rated Time Limit/7:30

Maze 39

JAWS
Rated Time Limit/5:30

2001: A SPACE ODYSSEY (HAL)

Rated Time Limit/4:30

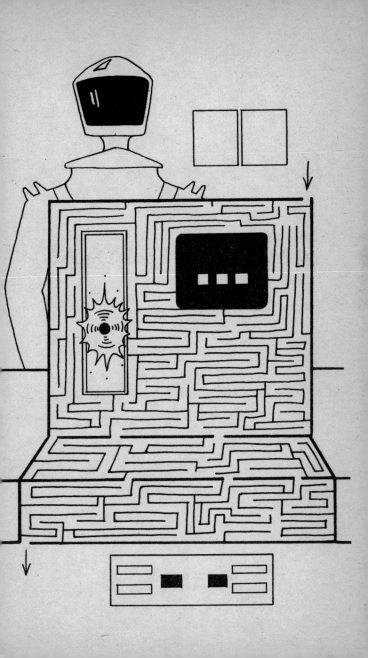

Maze 41

CAPTIVE WILD WOMAN
Rated Time Limit/7:00

Maze 42

THE PICTURE OF DORIAN GRAY

Rated Time Limit/5:00

SHE CREATURE
Rated Time Limit/6:00

THE MUMMY

Rated Time Limit/4:30

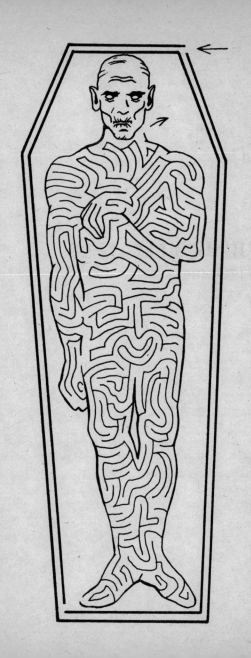

THE WOLFMAN
Rated Time Limit/5:30

Maze 46

I WAS A TEENAGE
WEREWOLF

Rated Time Limit/6:30

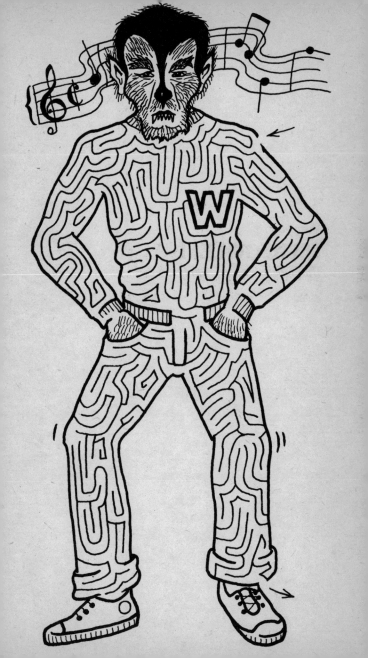

Maze 47

THE GOLEM

Rated Time Limit/3:00

THE HUNCHBACK OF NOTRE DAME

Rated Time Limit/7:30

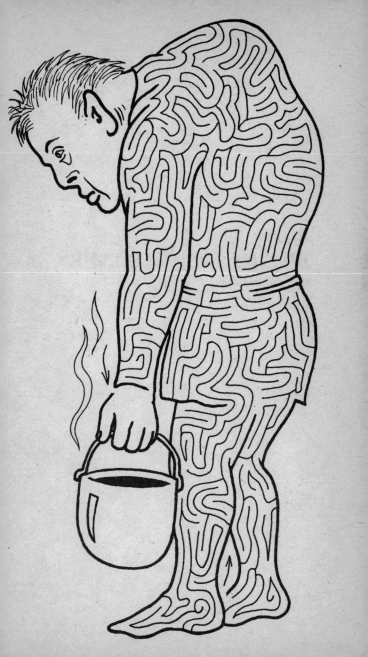

Maze 49

PLANET OF THE APES

Rated Time Limit/4:00

LONDON AFTER MIDNIGHT (VAMPIRE)

Rated Time Limit/7:00

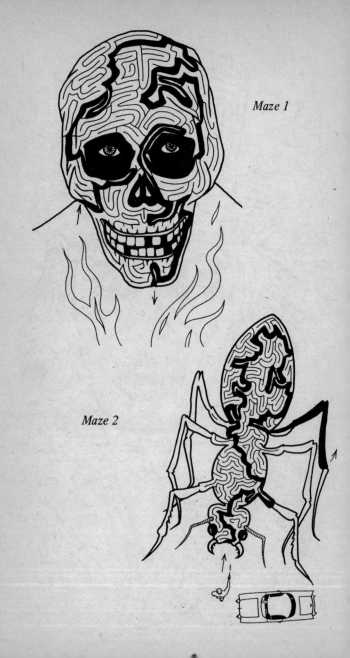

Maze 1

Maze 2

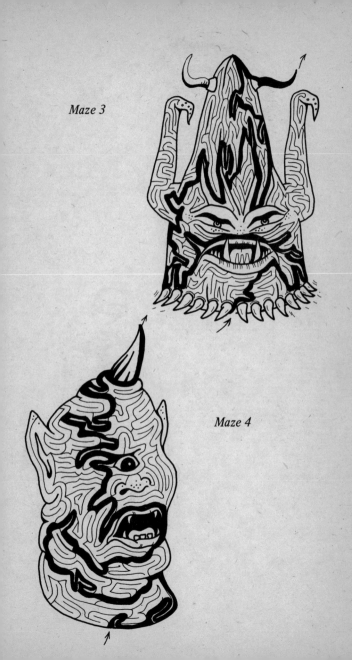

Maze 3

Maze 4

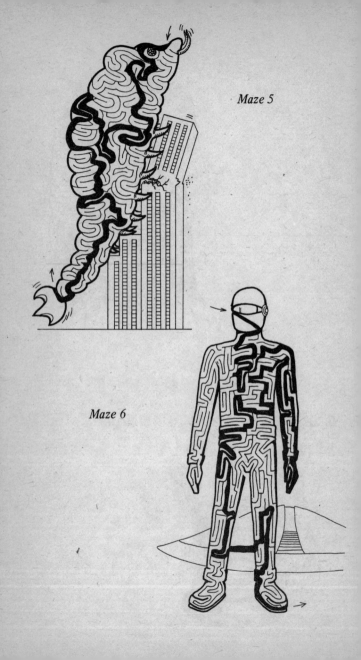

Maze 5

Maze 6

Maze 7

Maze 8

Maze 9

Maze 10

Maze 11

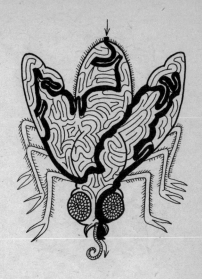

Maze 12

Maze 13

Maze 14

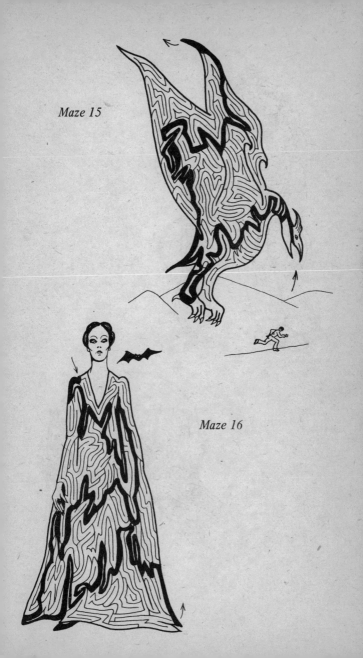

Maze 15

Maze 16

Maze 17

Maze 18

Maze 19

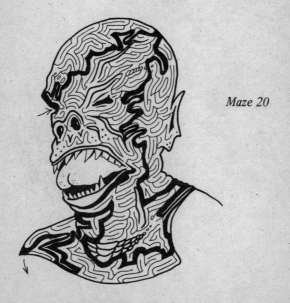

Maze 20

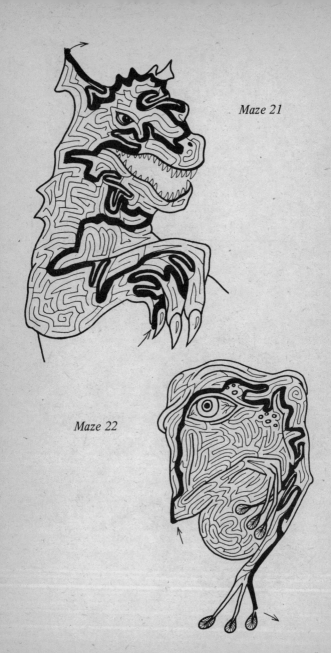

Maze 21

Maze 22

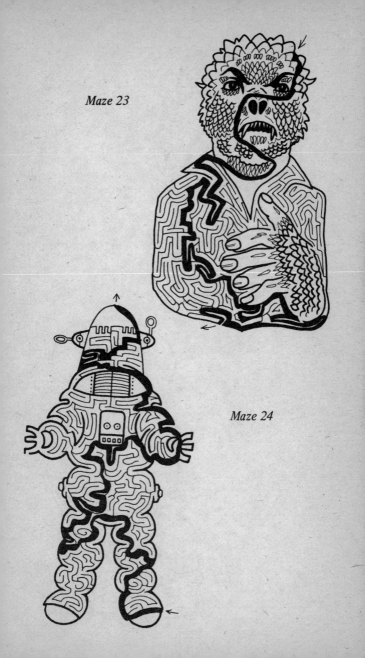

Maze 23

Maze 24

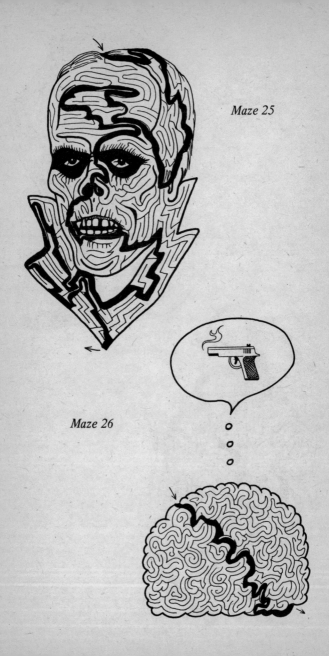

Maze 25

Maze 26

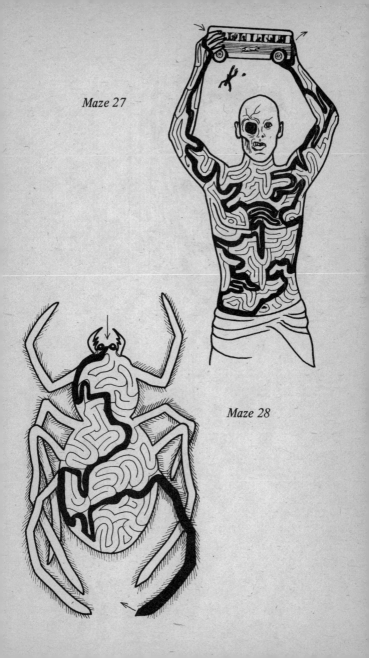

Maze 27

Maze 28

Maze 29

Maze 30

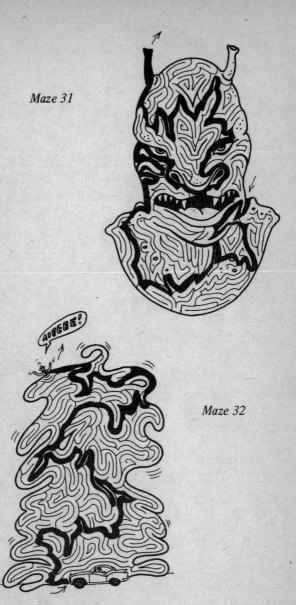

Maze 31

Maze 32

Maze 33

Maze 34

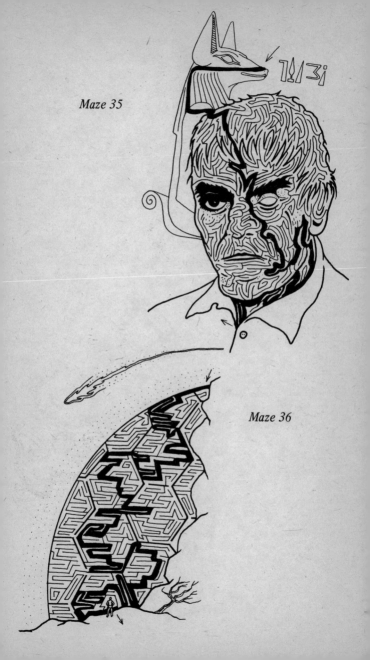

Maze 35

Maze 36

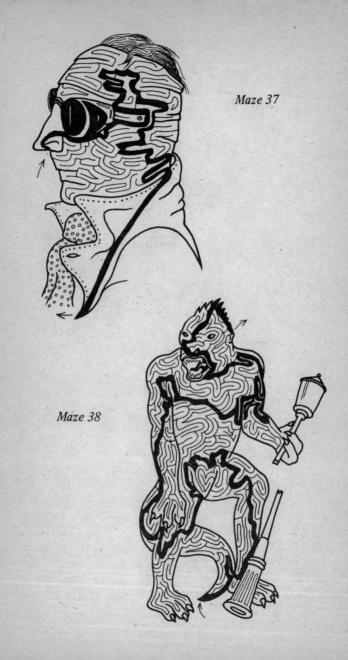

Maze 37

Maze 38

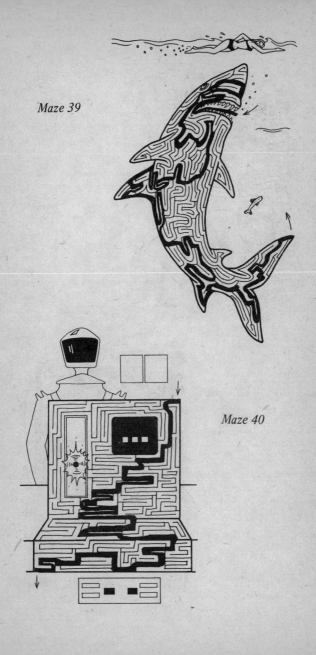

Maze 39

Maze 40

Maze 41

Maze 42

Maze 43

Maze 44

Maze 45

Maze 46

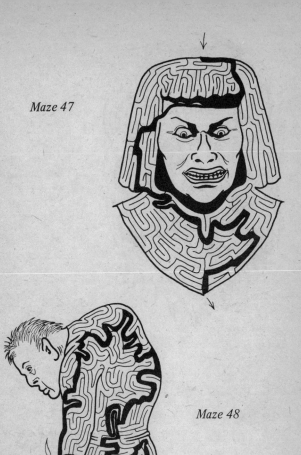

Maze 47

Maze 48

Maze 49

Maze 50